Rama and Sita

re-told by
Philip Page

Published in association with
The Basic Skills Agency

Hodder & Stoughton

A MEMBER OF THE HODDER HEADLINE GROUP

Acknowledgements
Cover: Philip Page
Illustrations: Philip Page

Orders; please contact Bookpoint Ltd, 39 Milton Park, Abingdon, Oxon OX14 4TD. Telephone: (44) 01235 400414, Fax: (44) 01235 400454. Lines are open from 9.00–6.00, Monday to Saturday, with a 24 hour message answering service. Email address: orders@bookpoint.co.uk

British Library Cataloguing in Publication Data
A catalogue record for this title is available from the British Library

ISBN 0 340 77680 3

First published 2000
Impression number 10 9 8 7 6 5 4 3 2 1
Year 2005 2004 2003 2002 2001 2000 1999

Typeset by GreenGate Publishing Services, Tonbridge, Kent.
Printed in Great Britain for Hodder and Stoughton Educational, a division of Hodder Headline Plc, 338 Euston Road, London NW1 3BH, by Atheneum Press, Gateshead, Tyne & Wear

Rama and Sita

Contents

The Four Brothers

Once upon a time there was a king.
He ruled over a great city in India.
The king's name was Dasaratha.
He had three wives and four sons.

The first wife's son was called Rama.
The second wife's son was called Bharata.
The third wife had two sons.
They were called Lakshmana and Satrughna.

The four brothers were close friends.
They were also great warriors and archers.

One day a wise man came to see the king.
'Please help me,' he said.
'There are some demons who attack me.'

The king said he would help.
He sent Rama and Lakshmana
to protect the wise man.

They travelled for many days.
They crossed great rivers and travelled
deep into a dark forest.

When they reached the place
where the wise man lived
he told them about the demons.
One was a female demon called Tadaka.
The other two were her sons.

Just then there was the sound of thunder.
The sky went dark.
The trees began to shake.
The animals and birds called out in fear.
'Tadaka is coming!' the wise man cried.

The demon appeared.
She was terrifying
but Rama and Lakshmana were not afraid.

Rama drew his bow and killed Tadaka
with a single arrow.

Tadaka's sons were very angry.
Rama had killed their mother.
They came for revenge
with an army of monsters.

Rama and Lakshmana ran to attack them.
Rama killed Tadaka's sons.
The monsters ran away in fear.

The wise man was very grateful.
He thanked the two brothers.
'You are brave men and skilful archers,'
he said.
'I can teach you more skills with the bow.
I will give you magic arrows.
Nobody will ever be able to defeat you.'

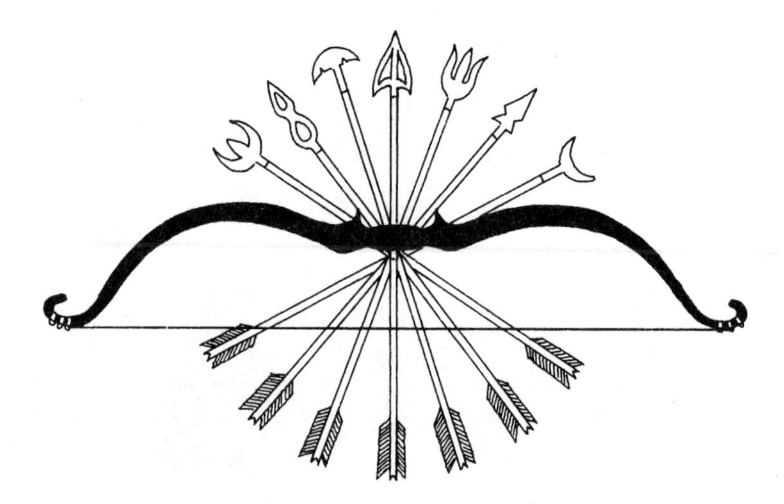

Rama Marries Sita

Rama and Lakshmana
travelled with the wise man
to another country.

The king of that country had
a beautiful daughter.
Her name was Sita.
Many kings and princes wanted to marry her.

As soon as Rama saw Sita
he fell in love with her.

The king planned a contest to see
who would marry his daughter.
He said that the man who could bend
and string the bow of the god Shiva
would be her husband.

One by one the kings and princes tried
but they could not even lift the bow.
Then it was Rama's turn.

He lifted the bow and bent it easily.
He was so strong he broke it!

Rama had won the contest.
He and Sita were married.
They returned to Rama's home land
where they lived happily together.

King Dasaratha's Promise

When Rama and Sita had been married
for twelve years,
King Dasaratha made a decision.

He knew he was getting old.
It was time for him to decide
who would be the next king.
He said that Rama would succeed him.

His second wife wanted her own son,
Bharata, to be the next king.

She reminded the king of a promise
he had made to her in the past.

She had saved his life in a battle.
He had promised to give her
anything she asked for.
Now she asked him
to make Bharata the king.
She wanted Rama sent into the forest
for fourteen years.

This was the last thing
King Dasaratha wanted to do!
He tried to get her to change her mind.
He said he would give her
anything else she wanted.

Rama said that the king
must not break his word.
He said he would do as she wanted.

Rama and Sita went away to live in the forest.
Lakshmana went with them.

Soon after this happened
King Dasaratha died.
Bharata went into the forest to find Rama.
He said that Rama was the rightful king.
He should return to the city.

'Our father made a promise,' said Rama.
'We must keep it.
I shall live here for fourteen years.
You must be the king.'

Bharata was sad but he agreed
to do what Rama wanted.
But he put Rama's slippers on the throne.
This would remind everybody that
Rama was the rightful king.

Ravana

While Rama, Sita and Lakshmana
were living in the forest,
a new demon came.
Her name was Surpanakha.
Although she was very ugly
she was very vain.

She fell in love with Rama.
She wanted to marry him.
Rama told her
he was already married to Sita.
The demon became very angry.
She threatened to kill Sita.

Rama told Lakshmana to punish the demon.
Lakshmana took his sword.
He cut off the demon's nose and ears.

Surpanakha screamed with pain.
She ran away. She went to her brother.
She told him what had happened to her.

Her brother was the King of Lanka.
He was a very powerful demon.
He had ten heads and twenty arms.

His name was Ravana.
Ravana made up his mind.
He would kidnap Sita
and marry her himself.

Ravana thought up a plan.
His uncle helped him.
His uncle changed into a beautiful deer.
Sita saw the deer.
She asked Rama to catch it for her.

While Rama was away in the forest
chasing the deer,
Ravana came and kidnapped Sita.
He forced her into his flying chariot
and took her away.

The Search for Sita

Ravana took Sita to his own land.
On their journey Sita dropped her jewels
one by one.
She hoped that Rama would find them
and follow the trail.

A great eagle saw what had happened.
The eagle was Rama's friend.
He flew after Ravana.

Ravana drew his sword.
He cut off the eagle's wings.
The eagle fell to the ground.
Before he died, he told Rama and Lakshmana
what Ravana had done.

And so the two brothers set out to rescue Sita.

On their journey
they came to a great mountain.
This was the land of the monkey king,
Sugriva. He sent four armies of monkeys
to search for Sita.

One army marched to the north.
The others went to the east,
the west and the south.
The army that went south
was led by the monkey god, Hanuman.

They came to the edge of a great ocean.
Suddenly, another eagle called down to him.
He told him that Ravana's kingdom
was on the other side of the ocean.
He had seen Ravana take Sita there.

Hanuman had the power to fly.
He flew over the ocean.
He searched until he found Sita.

He told her that Rama was on his way
to rescue her.

But Ravana and his army
of demons and monsters captured Hanuman.
He set fire to the monkey's tail
as a punishment.

Hanuman managed to escape.
He ran and ran.
The fire from his tail set fire to the houses.

He flew back across the ocean.
He told Rama he had found Sita.

The Great Battle

Hanuman ordered his army of monkeys
to build a bridge across the ocean.
Then Rama, Lakhsmana and Hanuman
crossed over the bridge into Lanka.

They saw Ravana and his army of demons
and monsters waiting for them.
They were a terrifying sight
but the brothers and Hanuman were not afraid.

The battle was very fierce.
At last Rama and Ravana faced each other.
Rama cut off Ravana's ten heads.
Still the demon king did not die.

Then Rama drew his bow.
He shot an arrow of fire at Ravana's heart.
Fire flashed across the sky. The earth shook
and Ravana died.

Sita is Tested

Rama had won the battle
but his troubles were not over.
People told him that Sita had been unfaithful.

Sita was very upset.
'How can I prove my innocence?' she said.
'You must walk through fire,' said Rama.
'If you are innocent, the fire will not harm you.'

Lakshmana was angry.
'Why are doing this?' he asked Rama.
'You know that Sita is innocent.'
'I know she is,' said Rama.
'But I want everybody else to see it.'

They built a great fire.
Sita walked into the fierce flames.
Agni, the God of Fire, protected her
and carried her out unharmed.

The Return Home

It was time for Rama and Sita to go home.
Rama wondered if his brother, Bharata,
would welcome them.
Would he let Rama be king?

After a long journey
they reached their home city.

It was dark
but people knew that they were coming.
They put lamps in the windows
of all their houses.
Rama and Sita came home to a city of lights!

Bharata was happy to see them.
'I have ruled your kingdom
while you were away,' he told Rama.

'Now the kingdom is yours.'
Rama and Sita were crowned.

Rama gave Sita a necklace of beautiful pearls.
'We must reward those who helped us,'
said Sita.
She took off the necklace.
She gave it to Hanuman.
Rama was pleased.

Rama ruled his kingdom well.
Everybody was happy.

One day Sita told Rama
she was expecting their baby.
Rama thought nothing could spoil
their happiness.
He was wrong.

Once again
people were spreading gossip about Sita.
'She proved her innocence once,' Rama said.
'What more can she do?'

But the gossip did not stop.
Rama called his brothers to him.
He told them what people were saying.

'There is only one thing I can do,' said Rama.
'I know Sita is innocent.
I know the child she bears is mine,
but I must send her away.
We cannot live together any more.'

He told Lakshmana to take Sita away.
Lakshmana did not want to do this
but he obeyed his brother.
He took Sita far away to another land.
'Tell Rama I have always loved him.
I have always been faithful to him.'

'Rama knows this,' said Lakshmana.
'He is not thinking of his own happiness.
He is thinking of the good of his kingdom.'

Sita gave birth to twin boys.
She called them Kusha and Lava.

Many years later
the two boys went to see Rama
They told him who they were.
Rama said it was time for Sita to return.

When she arrived she said,
'I will prove my innocence once again.
If I am innocent,
the Goddess of the Earth will take me'.

At that moment the ground opened.
The Goddess of the Earth,
rose out of the ground.
She sat on a throne
lifted by four great snakes.

The goddess took Sita's hand.
She sat her on the throne next to her.

Then they disappeared
down into the earth.
That was the last time
that anybody ever saw Sita.

Rama ruled over his kingdom
for many years.
He was a good king but without Sita
he was never happy again.

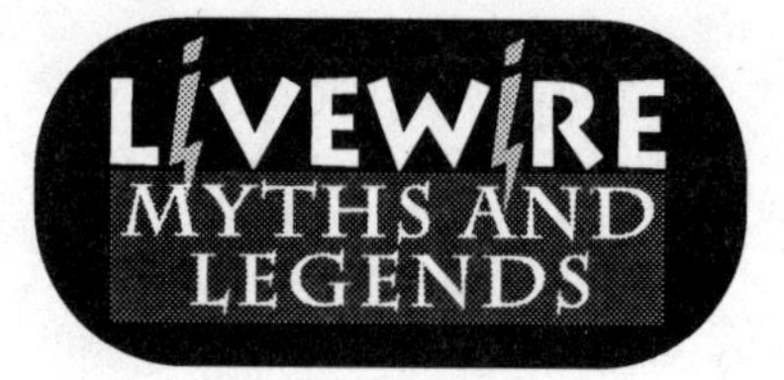

If you have enjoyed reading this book, you may be interested in other titles in the *Livewire* series.

King Oedipus
Medea
Hercules
Jason and the Golden Fleece
King Arthur
The Wooden Horse of Troy
Beowulf
The Odyssey
Robin Hood